I Can Play Music

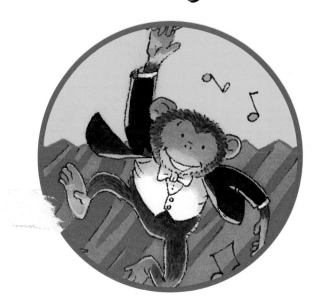

Written by Eva Gabriel
Illustrated by Clive Scruton

Scott Foresman

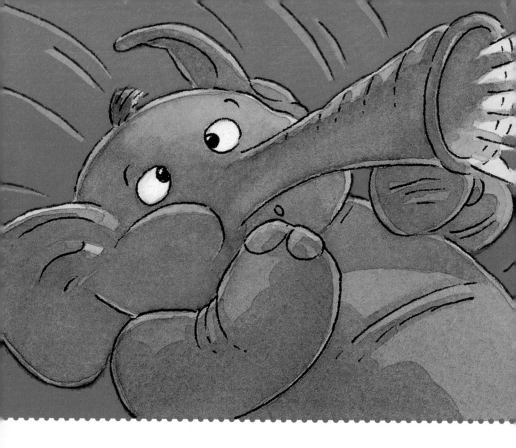

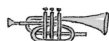

I can play a horn.

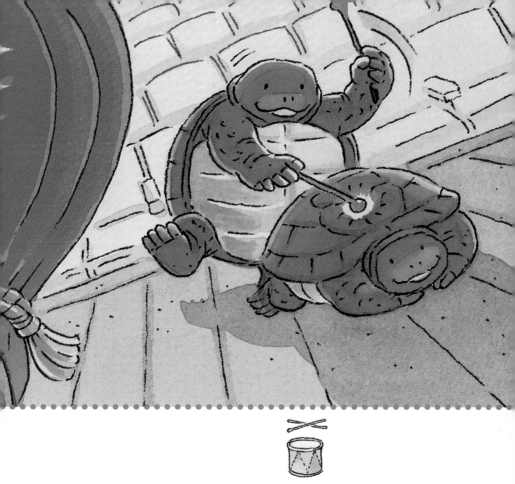

I can play a drum.

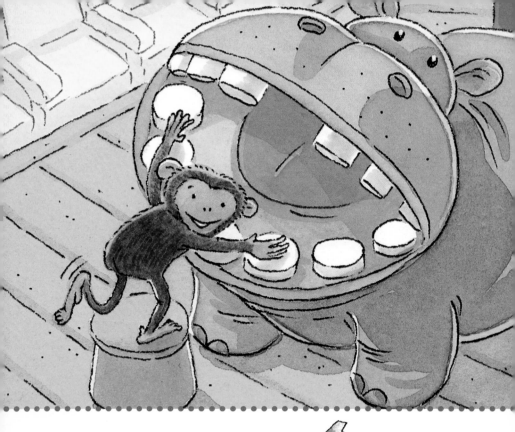

I can play a piano.

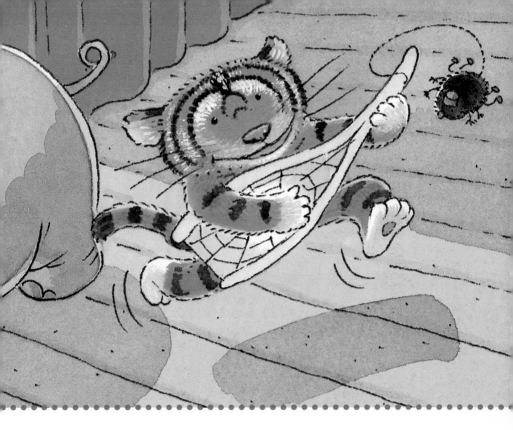

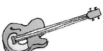

I can play a guitar.

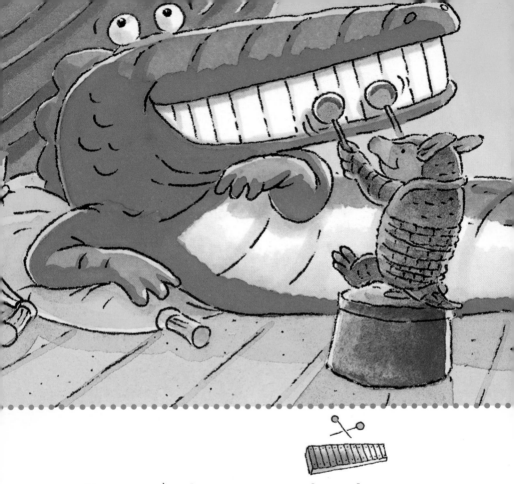

I can play a xylophone.

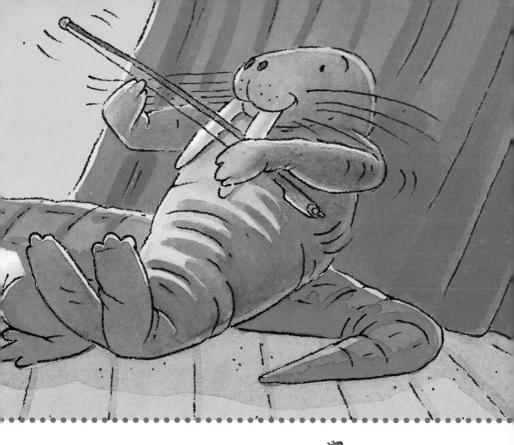

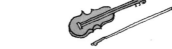

I can play a violin.

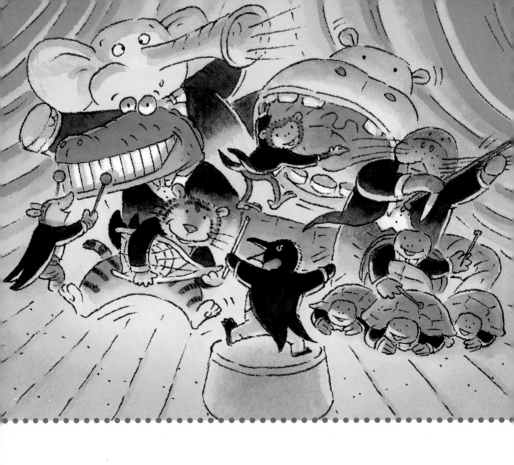

We can play music.